Bulk discounts available for educational purposes, reselling, gifts, or fundraising campaigns.
Email: author@thegoldenquest.com

Publisher's Cataloging-In-Publication Data
(Prepared by The Donohue Group, Inc.)

Names: Delisle, David, author. | Hanson, Travis, illustrator.
Title: The golden quest : your journey to a rich life / by David Delisle ;
        [illustrated by Travis Hanson].
Description: First edition. | [Victoria, British Columbia] : David Delisle, 2021. | Interest age level: 5 and up. | Summary: "... an
        illustrated adventure about a young boy who embarks on a Hero's Journey
        with his dog Shelby to discover the Golden Rules of Money"--Provided by
        publisher.
Identifiers: ISBN 9781777718909 (hardback) | ISBN 9781777718916 (ebook)
Subjects: LCSH: Boys--Juvenile fiction. | Money--Juvenile fiction. | Dogs-
        -Juvenile fiction. | Adventure and adventurers--Juvenile fiction. |
        CYAC: Boys--Fiction. | Money--Fiction. | Dogs--Fiction. |
        Adventure and adventurers--Fiction.
Classification: LCC PZ7.1.D4557 Go 2021 (print) | LCC PZ7.1.D4557 (ebook)
        | DDC [E]--dc23

the Golden Quest
Your Journey to a Rich Life

David Delisle

Dedicated to my boys, Will & Noah.

You were the inspiration to begin this journey and I wanted to thank you for all of your help, laughter and joy every step of the way. There is nothing that I'm more proud of than being your Dad.

You are my Awesome Stuff.

The Journey Begins

"A journey of a thousand miles
begins with a single step."
– Lao Tzu

4

ARE YOU SCARED, SHELBY?

WOOF WOOF

YEAH...

I'M NOT SCARED EITHER.

THE Awesome Stuff

"Wealth consists not in having great possessions, but in having few wants."
– Epictetus

14

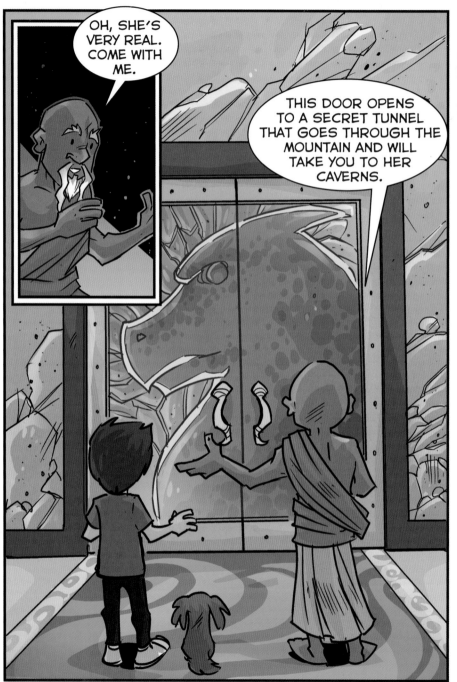

20

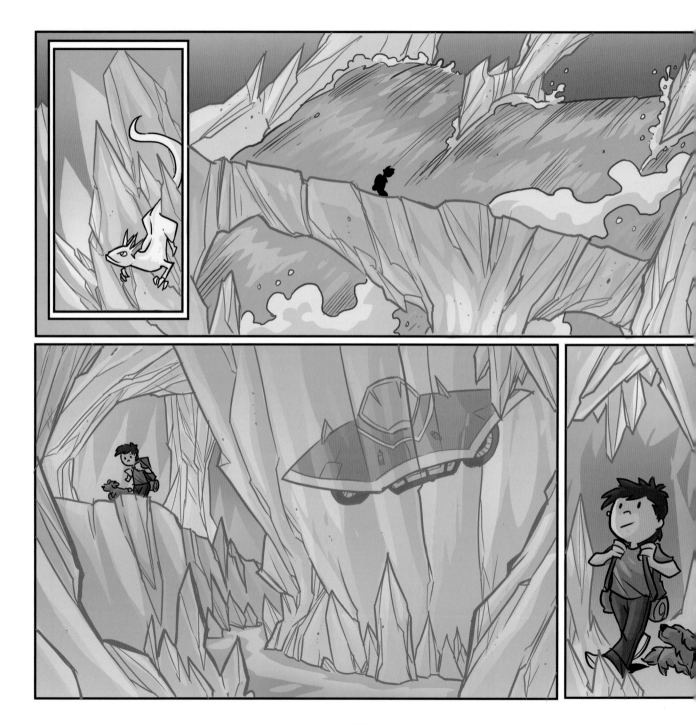

25

26

28

29

30

33

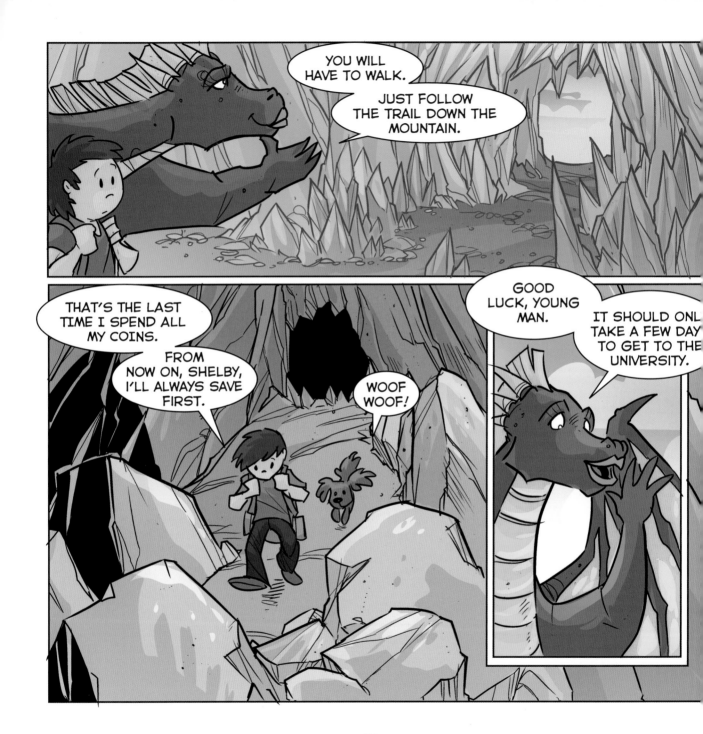

Compound Interest

The most powerful force in the Universe.

"Money makes money. And the money that money makes, makes money."
–attributed to
Benjamin Franklin

WOOF
WOOF!

HI! I'M
HERE FOR
THE JOB YOU
POSTED.

38

39

41

DID THE DRAGON OF THE CRYSTAL CAVERNS SEND YOU?

EXCELLENT. FOR TODAY'S LESSON, I'LL TEACH YOU HOW TO GROW YOUR SAVINGS EVEN MORE...

YES. SHE TAUGHT ME TO "ALWAYS SAVE FIRST" IF I WANT MY SAVINGS TO GROW.

...BY NOT LETTING YOUR SAVINGS SIT AROUND DOING NOTHING.

INSTEAD, INVEST YOUR SAVINGS.

INVEST? WHAT IS THAT?

IT'S LIKE SENDING YOUR SAVINGS TO WORK.

43

44

46

49

56

SO, ONE DAY...

...SHE LEFT HER FORGE BEHIND...

...TO GO SEARCH FOR THE HIDDEN TREASURE OF...

the Final Lesson

"Time is the most valuable thing
a (person) can spend."
    – Theophrastus

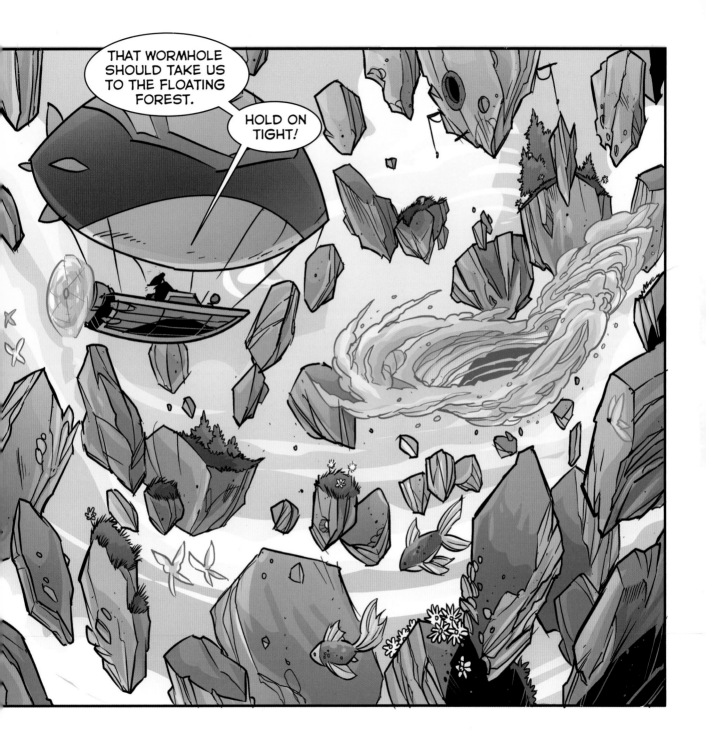

69

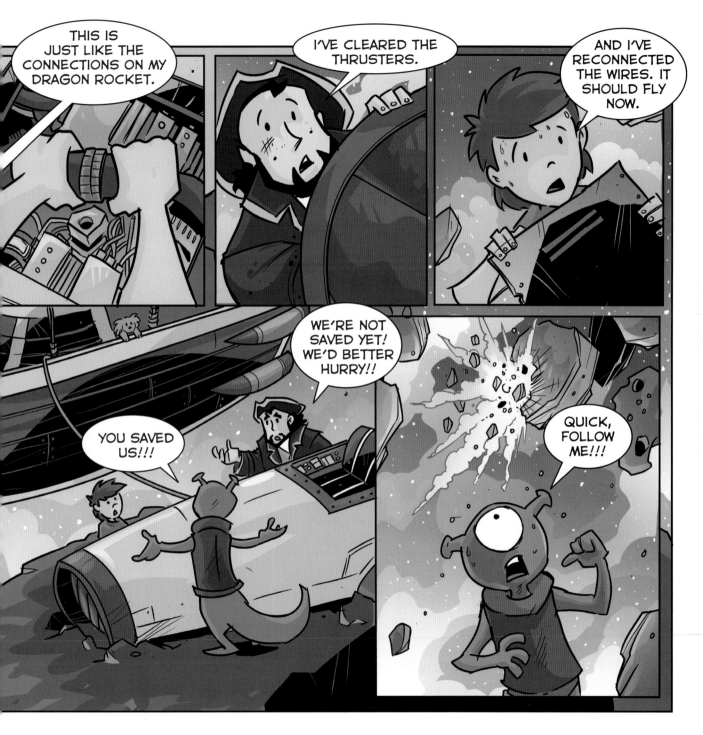

THE GOLDEN RULES

Golden Rule #1: Only buy the awesome stuff.

Golden Rule #2: Always save first.

Golden Rule #3: Send your savings to work TODAY.

Golden Rule #4: Give and you'll have more.

Follow the Golden Rules of Money so you'll have more freedom for what's most important to YOU. The Awesome Stuff.

I wanted to THANK YOU again for joining me on this journey.

If you know of anyone that would benefit from reading The Golden Quest and learning the Golden Rules of Money, it would mean so so much to me if you shared this story with them. I'm also available for speaking engagements to help spread this message. With your help, we can change the way we think about money and what it means to live a rich life.

Bulk discounts are available for orders of 10 copies or more.
Please contact me for more details.
Email: author@thegoldenquest.com

Only Buy the Awesome Stuff™
www.onlybuytheawesomestuff.com